Richard Edmonds' interest in fossils began at the age of eight on Charmouth Beach and led him to study geology at the University of Hull from 1980 to 1983. After graduation he worked in the North Sea Oil Industry before moving to the field of countryside interpretation, initially as a volunteer with the National Trust for Scotland on the Isle of Arran and, in 1986, as warden of the Charmouth Heritage Coast Centre. During the next eleven years he led countless numbers of people onto the local beaches of West Dorset in search of fossils. In 1997 Richard took up a new post as Jurassic Coast Project Officer, a feasibility study looking to promote sustainable tourism based on the internationally important geology of Dorset's Jurassic Coast.

Following page
Monmouth Beach, west of Lyme Regis is an excellent place to discover fossils and many, like this giant ammonite, though far too large to collect, offer an introduction to Dorset's famous fossils.

DISCOVER DORSET

FOSSILS

RICHARD EDMONDS

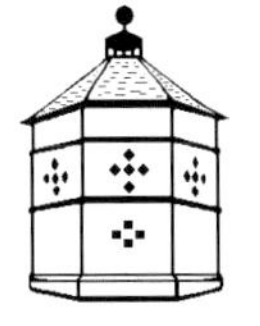

THE DOVECOTE PRESS

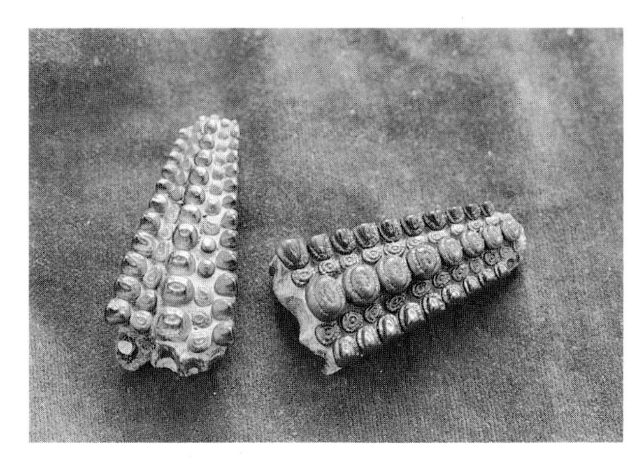

Beautiful fish palates, *Gyrodus cuveri*, from the Lower Kimmeridge Clay at Ferrybridge, Portland. These are sets of teeth for crushing prey.

First published in 1999 by The Dovecote Press Ltd
Stanbridge, Wimborne, Dorset BH21 4JD

ISBN 1 874336 65 2

Series designed by Humphrey Stone

Typeset in Sabon by The Typesetting Bureau
Wimborne, Dorset
Printed and bound by Baskerville Press, Salisbury, Wiltshire

A CIP catalogue record for this book is available from the British Library

3 5 7 9 8 6 4

CONTENTS

WHAT ARE FOSSILS AND HOW DO THEY FORM?

Fossils have long been a source of curiosity and fascination, but only in the last two hundred years has the science of palaeontology begun to unravel the story they tell. In the eighteenth century, fossil collectors at Charmouth and Lyme Regis were known as 'curimen' and the objects they traded were simply 'curiosities'. Today we treat these marvels of nature with the attention they merit, for Dorset's fossils provide a window into the ancient past stretching back over 200 million years and are contained within one of the most geologically diverse counties in Britain.

Even after two centuries of collecting and study, new discoveries continue to be made. A huge volume of rock underlies the county and the amount that has been eroded or quarried since the first pioneers began collecting is a minute fraction of the total. Indeed, perhaps the greatest attraction of fossil collecting and research is that there is always the chance of discovering something entirely new to science, something no one else has ever seen before.

Fossils are quite simply the remains of plants and animals that have become buried in sediments that later turned to rock. Most are of animals that lived in the sea, simply because the process of fossilisation is far more likely to occur under water than on land.

When a large sea creature such as an ichthyosaur (a dolphin-like reptile) died, it sank to the sea floor where the soft parts normally

Top left A perfectly preserved lobster from the Lower Jurassic rocks at Charmouth.

Left A fish from the Kimmeridge Clay. The quality of preservation and completeness of fossils provides clues about the environments in which the rocks formed and the events leading up to, and during the process of fossilisation. Was this fish attacked by predators before it became fossilised?

rotted away. Sediments such as mud washed from the land settled on the sea floor, burying the skeleton. Further sediments built up, compacting the soft mud until it slowly turned to rock. Crystals and minerals transformed the bones into harder materials. Over millions of years the rocks were heaved up to form land and became exposed to erosion, releasing the fossilised bones for us to find today.

On land, fossilisation usually takes place in swamps, rivers, flood plains and lagoons where sediments settle and build up over time. One of the most extraordinary forms of land-based fossils are those of dinosaur footprints, which only become preserved as a result of a specific set of circumstances, beginning with a drop in water level causing sediments to become exposed on the shores of a swamp or lagoon. Dinosaurs walked across the soft mud, leaving a trail of footprints. The mud then became baked in the tropical heat, hardening enough to retain the impressions of the footprints when water levels rose again. Further sediments filled the depressions, creating a cast of the footprint, facing down into the sediment. As a result, many footprints are casts of the print rather than impressions.

Different environments lead to different forms of preservation. Shallow seas subject to strong currents may lead to the rapid burial of sea shells, creating a rock such as the Trigonia Beds at Osmington, which is packed with fossils. However, under such conditions, it is unlikely that larger animals will be well preserved because their skeletons were usually broken up by the action of the currents. Taken to an extreme, some fossils may be broken and damaged during or even after fossilisation and may be reworked by erosion. The Lower Jurassic, Middle Lias Junction Bed at Eype, west of Bridport, is a classic example where not only the fossils but also associated pebbles, complete with borings, have been eroded and redeposited to create a distinctive and fascinating rock layer or strata.

Some animals, by their very nature, are more likely to become fossilised than others. Those with durable hard parts, such as crinoids, can survive transportation in currents. As a result scattered accumulations of the plate-like structures that make up their bodies are common in certain rocks such as the sandstones of the Middle Lias. Other animals may become fossilised as a result of the way they lived. Burrowing creatures such as worms, crustaceans, sea urchins

The Roach Stone, Portland Limestone, Isle of Portland. Here, after fossilisation the bivalve and snail shells have been dissolved away, leaving internal moulds and external casts, complete with details of the shell structure and decoration.

and certain bivalves live within the sediment and are already buried. They therefore stand a far better chance of becoming fossilised.

After burial, the porosity of the rock has an important role to play in the fossilisation process. Highly porous rocks such as sandstones and limestones are subject to the flow of groundwater. This can result in the shells of fossils being totally dissolved away leaving a mould of the inside of the shell and a cast of the outside within the rock itself. On Portland this type of preservation is superbly developed in the Roach Stone, a limestone packed with the casts and moulds of sea shells. The exact opposite can also happen, even within the same rock type in a different place. At St Aldhelm's Head, Purbeck, the equivalent of the Roach is found, but here the hollows left by the shells have been filled with blue calcite crystal, creating a beautiful decorative rock known as Spangle.

A BRIEF TOUR OF DORSET'S GEOLOGY

The importance of Dorset as a source of some of the finest fossils in the world is due to the diversity of the geology exposed along the coast and the variety of outcrops across the county. The rocks of Dorset cover three periods of geological time, the Jurassic, Cretaceous and Tertiary, recording some 160 million years of earth history from about 200 million years ago to 40 million years ago. A number of younger sedimentary deposits are found lying on these older rocks, and they largely consist of sands and gravels deposited in the last two million years as the landscape emerged from the last Ice Age into the coast and countryside we recognise today.

The geological wealth of the county is due to a simple feature; the overall dip of the rocks is gently to the east and as a result very different rocks are exposed, from the oldest in the west to the youngest in the east. Dorset's rocks formed in a huge and slowly subsiding area of the earth's crust known as the Wessex Basin. Several thousand metres of rock were deposited as the basin slowly subsided. Later earth movements heaved the rocks up to form land and in the process produced both the gentle overall easterly dip and the dramatic folds visible on the Isle of Purbeck. The broadest expression of this feature can be seen in the three distinctive landscapes that dominate the county. The clay vales and rolling countryside of West Dorset are formed from soft Lower Jurassic rocks. Across the centre of the county runs a broad swath of Cretaceous Chalk that gives rise to downland, while the lowland heaths in the east of the county are formed from clays, sands and gravels of Tertiary age.

JURASSIC

The start of the Jurassic took place about 210 million years ago when sea levels rose to flood an area of desert that existed in Triassic times. Global temperatures were higher than today and Britain lay at a latitude similar to that of modern Florida. The process of plate tectonics (the slow but immensely powerful process that moves the

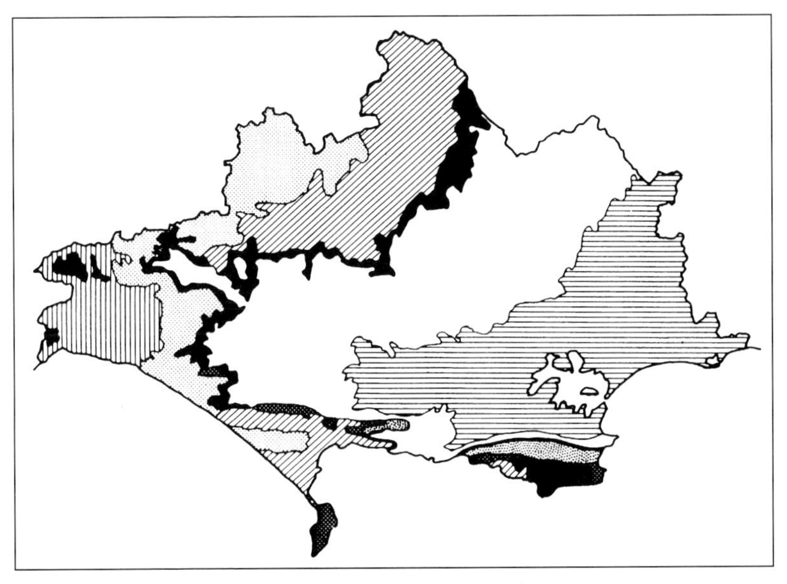

A simplified map of the geology of Dorset.

- Tertiary rocks (clays, sands & gravels).
- Chalk (limestone).
- Lower Greensand, Gault & Upper Greensand (clays & sands).
- Wealden (clays, silts, sands & grits).
- Portland Sand & Stone & Purbeck Limestone Group (limestones & clays).
- Kellaways Beds, Oxford Clay, Corallian & Kimmeridge Clay (limestones & clays).
- Inferior Oolite, Fuller's Earth, Frome Clay, Forest Marble & Cornbrash (limestone & clays).
- Lower, Middle & Upper Lias (thin limestones, clays, silts & sands).

thin crust, including the continents, over its surface) has carried Britain to its more northerly latitude.

Initially the sea was quite deep and muddy, allowing thick layers of clay rocks with thin bands of limestone to form. As time passed the sea became shallower, leading to the deposition of sands and then limestones, known as the Inferior Oolite, that are of Middle Jurassic age. This pattern of deposition is repeated again through the Middle and Upper Jurassic rocks and is superbly displayed in the cliffs of Portland and Houns-tout in Purbeck. Here the Kimmeridge Clay, another thick, deep water deposit, passes into the Portland Sands and then the Portland Limestone, which again is an oolitic limestone (on Portland) that formed in a shallow sea.

Dinosaurs were alive throughout the Jurassic period but because Dorset lay under the sea during most of this time, their remains are not 'common' until the late Jurassic and early Cretaceous, when sea levels dropped and a landmass emerged. Directly above the Portland Limestones are the Purbeck Beds, at whose base lie a series of fossilised soils and one of Dorset's most spectacular geological features, known as the Fossil Forest, that today is visible east of Lulworth Cove, on Portland and in a few inland sites.

CRETACEOUS

The Purbeck Beds are a complex sequence of limestones and clays that display enormous variation, reflecting the shallow water and at times arid environments in which they were deposited. These rocks are magnificently exposed in Durlston Bay, Swanage, where they are famous for fossils, particularly fish, insects, reptiles and early mammals. They also yield numerous dinosaur footprints and trackways, especially from the working quarries around the Swanage area. The overlying Wealden Beds are a thick sequence of soft, multi-coloured clays and sands that reach a great thickness in the east of the county.

Towards the end of the Lower Cretaceous marine conditions returned in which the Lower Greensand was deposited. During this time a period of complex earth movements occurred allowing uplift and erosion to take place before the deposition of the Gault Clay and

The cliffs in the foreground and the spectacular sea stacks of Mupe Rocks are formed from Portland Limestone and Lower Purbeck Beds of late Jurassic age. The banded cliffs of Bacon Hole in the distance consist of younger Purbeck Beds of Cretaceous age. The junction between the Jurassic and Cretaceous lies in between, but its exact location remains a subject of debate.

Dorset's heathland character is due to the soft and well drained sands, grits and clays of Tertiary age that underlie the east of the county. Occasional areas contain well-cemented sands and grits that weather out to form sarsen stones such as the Agglestone on Godlingston Heath, Studland.

Upper Greensand. The relationship between these rocks and older deposits is therefore complicated by a gap in the rock record created by erosion. Further complications are present in that the degree of erosion varied greatly across Dorset. In Purbeck the gap is relatively small, but in West Dorset virtually the entire Jurassic sequence has been eroded away and the Gault and Upper Greensand lie directly on rocks of Lower Jurassic age.

The final and most significant rock of Cretaceous age is without doubt the Chalk, a massive layer of limestone composed almost entirely of microscopic calcareous plant remains known as coccoliths. Chalk formed in a vast sea surrounded by a dry desert from which virtually no sediments were derived, allowing the build up of this pure white limestone, one of the most striking and widespread rocks in Europe.

TERTIARY

The Tertiary period began 65 million years ago and was marked, in Dorset, by a period of prolonged erosion, deeply weathering the Chalk and removing any evidence of the Cretaceous – Tertiary extinction that wiped out the dinosaurs and many other life forms. Early in the Tertiary period, sands, clays and gravels where deposited on the eroded surface of the Chalk. The climate was still tropical through much of this time and most of the rocks formed in extensive river deltas and swamps that were occasionally submerged by the sea.

Earth movements which formed the Alps in southern Europe later folded the rocks of Dorset, creating enormous structures such as the Purbeck monocline. This huge kink in the rock layers can be seen at Durdle Door, Lulworth Cove and Worbarrow Bay. It then runs inland across Purbeck, through Corfe Castle, on to Ballard Down and then under the sea to the Needles on the Isle of Wight.

Towards the end of the Tertiary period, the sandwich of rocks that had accumulated over the previous 160 million years was heaved up yet again to form land and became subject to another period of prolonged erosion. This produced a vast flat landscape, the remains of which can still be seen in the level hill tops of West Dorset and East Devon.

Finally, some 2 million years ago, the Ice Age started and although ice sheets never covered Dorset the land was subject to perma frost, while huge glaciers lay to the north, along a line from the River Thames to the River Severn. These processes cut through the rocks to create the landscape that we see and enjoy today.

FOSSILS: CLUES TO THE PAST

DETERMINING PAST ENVIRONMENTS

Fossils provide geologists with vital clues to the environments within which the rocks formed. For instance, the extinct ammonite is closely related to modern day nautilus, cuttlefish and squid, a group of animals only found in the sea. It is therefore reasonable to assume that rocks containing ammonites formed in a marine environment.

Several of the clay rocks found within the Jurassic sequence contain black, laminated and bituminous (oil rich) shales. These rocks typically contain fossils of creatures from the open water, but lack any bottom-dwelling animals such as bivalves and gastropods. This suggests that the sea floor was stagnant and poisonous to life when the rocks were forming, precisely the conditions under which oil forms. When plankton settled onto a stagnant sea floor the process of decay was slowed long enough for the organic matter to be buried within the sediments. Millions of years later a combination of heat and pressure 'cooked' the plankton into oil in a process still not fully understood today. Several of the rocks exposed along the Dorset coast are the sources of oil. The oil found under Poole Harbour originated within the oldest Jurassic rocks, the Lower Lias.

The conditions that gave rise to the formation of oil also led to the exceptional preservation of fossils, including soft parts such as skin, intestines and muscles. However some of the most important fossils to the geologist contain no part of the original animal at all. Trace fossils, the tracks and marks left by animals, allow accurate descriptions to be made of the environment in which the rocks were deposited. Take the trace fossil *Thalassinoides*, a distinctive, branching burrow probably made by a crustacean such as a shrimp and commonly found in rocks such as the Osmington Oolite at Osmington. Identical burrows can be found in shallow tropical waters today, allowing geologists to speculate with some degree of

'Fossil' ripple marks from the Lower Purbeck Beds on Portland indicate that the rocks formed in shallow water across which the wind blew.

confidence that the rocks at Osmington formed in a similar tropical sea.

Some natural features are referred to as having been fossilised. Take for instance the beautiful 'fossil' ripple-marked Purbeck Beds high on the west cliffs of Portland, and on the promontory of Durdle Door and Man O' War Cove. The ripples clearly indicate that a current flowed across the soft sediments as they were deposited millions of years ago. But how deep was the water? The question is answered by examining other 'fossil' sedimentary features associated with these particular rocks. Some of the Purbeck Beds contain fissures similar to the mud cracks you might find on the edge of a dried up pond in summer. Therefore geologists can tell that the rocks were laid down in shallow water that occasionally dried out. This is confirmed by the occurrence of salt pseudomorphs, casts of cubic salt crystals that indicate that evaporation was high, concentrating salt from sea water and creating hypersaline conditions in which the crystals could grow. The most dramatic proof of this interpretation comes in the form of dinosaur footprints that clearly indicate that the water was either very shallow or dried out entirely.

EVOLUTION

Most of us now accept the theory of Charles Darwin that life evolved over millions of years from simple forms into the staggering diversity of plants and animals that we see around us today. The earth itself is about 4,600 million years old and the earliest known life forms date back 3,000 million years. The Jurassic period only started 210 million years ago, relatively late in the evolutionary story of life on earth. For the next 145 million years dinosaurs ruled the land and marine reptiles such as ichthyosaurs swam in the sea. Despite successfully adapting to their respective environments, both were ultimately doomed, reminding us that evolution is a challenge to all species.

A number of animals that were also alive in the Jurassic seas have fared rather better. The humble scallop shells found within the Lower Jurassic rocks of Thornecombe Beacon or the high-spired

This scallop from the Lower Jurassic rocks at Seatown is almost identical to modern day shell fish and yet it lived within a sea occupied by marine reptiles such as the ichthyosaur and plesiosaur, both of which are now extinct.

The 'Ammonite Graveyard', Monmouth Beach, Lyme Regis. Did some natural disaster overwhelm a whole shoal of ammonites that once swam in the Jurassic sea?

snails from the Portland Roach are almost exactly the same as those we find today. This mixture of extinct and modern life forms found living side by side during the Jurassic period reflects the state of evolution during the Mesozoic epoch (middle time) of the earth's long history.

The theory of evolution suggests that plants and animals adapt to change through genetic variation and mutations that prove beneficial by creating an advantage over others, leading to 'the survival of the fittest'. However, many species in the fossil record appear to replace each other almost instantaneously with very few, if any, specimens displaying features of both the original and new species. The reason for this is simple, geological time is measured in millions of years during which countless generations of plants and animals have lived and died. Relatively speaking, few animals or plants have become trapped in the fossil record as most were eaten or destroyed in the daily struggle for survival. Therefore, when compared with geological time, changes in individuals and the evolution of new species are short term events, hence the scarcity of specimens displaying transitional features.

Some animals appear to defy evolution altogether and are referred to as 'living fossils'. A good example is one of nature's most efficient predators, the shark. So well adapted to their environment are sharks that they have hardly changed in 300 million years. The survival of other living fossils is harder to explain. Take for instance the ammonite's close relative, the nautilus, whose fossils can be found within the large blocks of Blue Lias on Monmouth Beach, west of Lyme Regis. Ammonites are long extinct but the nautilus survives on coral reefs in the Indo-Pacific region today. By day they hide in deep water but at night they venture across the reefs in search of food. Perhaps the ability of the nautilus to dive to comparatively deep depths allowed it to escape the evolutionary pressures that caused the extinction of the ammonites, but no one can be certain.

A nautilus from Charmouth. The nautilus is a 'living fossil' that has changed very little in the last four hundred million years. Nautilus can be found throughout most of Dorset's Jurassic and Cretaceous rocks and yet animals with an identical shell still swim in the Pacific Ocean today.

Asteroceras obtusum identifies the Obtusum Zone within the Lower Jurassic, Lower Lias.

USING FOSSILS TO DATE ROCKS

Because animals have evolved through time each rock layer or stratum contains a unique and often distinctive assemblage of fossils. On the broadest scale, trilobites (woodlouse-like creatures) are only found in rocks of the Cambrian to Permian periods, while ammonites are restricted to rocks of the Jurassic and Cretaceous periods. Therefore rocks that contain ammonites can only be of Jurassic or Cretaceous age (unless the fossil was eroded and redeposited in younger rocks). This broad principal can be applied with a great deal of precision by using individual species of rapidly evolving animals to identify specific periods of geological time.

Ammonites are ideal as 'zone fossils'; fossils whose presence in a rock determines a precise period of geological time. Take the ammonite *Asteroceras obtusum*, which is found within a thin layer of rock within the Black Ven Marls around the Charmouth area. The same ammonite can be found on the Yorkshire coast near Robin Hood's Bay, allowing geologists to conclude that the rocks at both localities are of exactly the same geological age. By using this method, the Jurassic period has been divided into over seventy ammonite zones that identify periods of time of less than a million years in duration, and it is Dorset's coast that has provided many of the exposures and specimens upon which this work is based.

DORSET'S FOSSILS

Due to the many different environments that have existed over the last 160 million years in what is now Dorset, the rocks of the county contain an abundance of different fossil life forms, including representatives from virtually all the major animal and plant groups.

VERTEBRATES
(animals with backbones)

FISH

Virtually all the fossil fish found in the rocks of Dorset belong to ancient armoured species that are distant ancestors to those that swim in the oceans today. Take *Dapedium*, the 'classic' fish from the Lower Jurassic of West Dorset, which looks so life-like because its scales are heavily armoured. When the fish died, it's internal soft parts rotted away but the exterior appearance changed little. In contrast, most modern fish are commonly fossilised as a skeleton with just the impression of the scales preserved within the surrounding rock. Sharks and rays have a skeleton composed of cartilage which normally rots away during the process of fossilisation, leaving nothing more than the hard teeth and dorsal spines.

REPTILES

By the Jurassic period, the reptiles had evolved into the largest and most advanced group of animals. If the dinosaurs ruled the land, the sea was the kingdom of ichthyosaurs and the huge pliosaur. These reptiles are among the most spectacular fossils to be found in Dorset and numerous specimens from the coast, most notably ichthyosaurs from the Lyme Regis area, have pride of place in both national and international collections.

Fish such as *Dapedium politum* from the Lower Jurassic rocks of West Dorset look so life-like because they had armoured scales that became perfectly preserved after death.

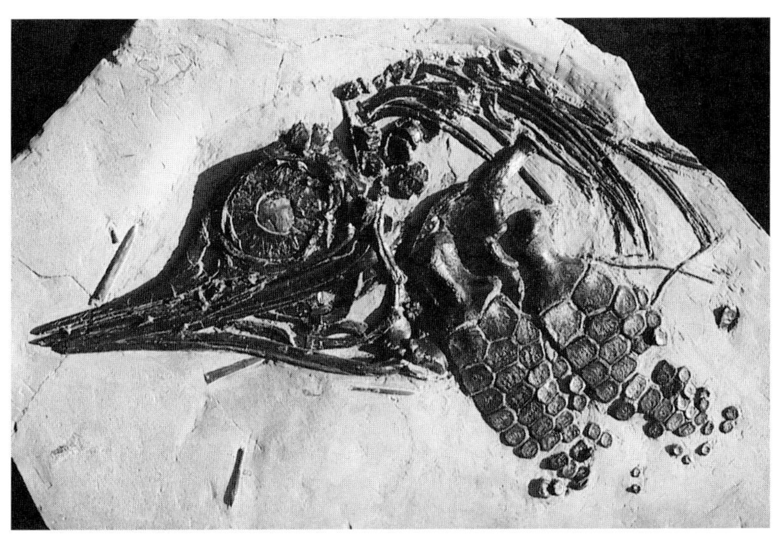

A new species of Ichthyosaur from the Lower Jurassic rocks below Golden Cap discovered in 1994. Despite over two hundred years of fossil collecting, new finds continue to be made each year.

Ichthyosaurs were dolphin-like reptiles that could reach 10 metres long and were swift, agile hunters. Complete specimens are relatively rare, and the commonest finds are isolated backbones. Numerous species show a wide range of adaptations to different hunting techniques, but most probably chased ammonites, belemnites and fish in the open water. Specimens have been found with perfect baby embryos inside their bodies, suggesting that they gave birth to live young.

Plesiosaurs could reach over 12 metres in length and most species had a long neck and tail, a large barrel-shaped body and huge fins. They are thought to have come ashore to lay their eggs, which might explain why they are so much rarer than ichthyosaurs. During much of the Jurassic, the nearest land to Dorset was many miles away to the north. Interestingly, the Lower Jurassic rocks of Somerset yield a richer fauna of plesiosaurs, supporting the theory that they were animals of the coastal waters rather than the open sea.

Pliosaurs were massively built reptiles with short necks and bulky bodies. They evolved in Upper Jurassic times and are therefore best known from the rocks in Purbeck and on Portland. Quite recently a lower jaw was found at Kimmeridge which was over five feet long, while other impressive finds include teeth up to six inches in length. This was a formidable creature, growing to over 10 metres long.

In addition to bones of marine reptiles, their fossil droppings, known as **coprolites**, are not uncommon, and many of them are rich in fish-scales and bones.

Dinosaurs thrived throughout the Jurassic and Cretaceous periods. During most of this time the area that is now Dorset was under water and therefore most of Dorset's fossils are of sea creatures. Despite this, some dinosaur corpses were washed into the sea, where they became fossilised alongside much humbler creatures such as ammonites. *Scelidosaurus* is one of the earliest dinosaurs and, until recently, was only known from a handful of specimens recovered from the Lower Jurassic rocks around Charmouth. A four legged, armoured herbivore up to 4 metres long, it may be an early relative of *Stegosaurus*. In contrast, the three-toed, carnivorous dinosaur, *Megalosaurus*, is known from the Upper Jurassic Kimmeridge Clay, near Weymouth at Ferrybridge, and the Kimmeridge area.

During the late Jurassic and early Cretaceous periods, a low-lying

Scelidosaurus was an armoured dinosaur best known from a handful of specimens from the Lower Jurassic rocks at Charmouth. In 1984 a specimen was found complete with skin and scales.

landmass surrounded by tropical swamps and lagoons emerged in the 'Dorset' area. Rocks formed at this time record evidence of dinosaurs in the form of trace fossils, individual footprints and spectacular trackways where the dinosaurs walked across the shores of the ancient swamps. Such fossils are found where the Purbeck Beds near Swanage are exposed along the coast and within the numerous small quarries of the area.

Flying reptiles or pterosaurs, are among the rarest fossils. All animals that fly require light bodies and therefore pterosaurs (just like birds today) had hollow bones. A pterosaur washed into the sea was far more likely to float than sink, reducing the chances of it's delicate skeleton becoming fossilised. The Lower Jurassic rocks of West Dorset contain *Dimorphodon*, but it is only known from a handful of fragmentary bones and one nearly complete specimen found near Lyme Regis by the pioneering fossil collector Mary Anning in 1829. The Kimmeridge Clay is the richest source of pterosaurs in Dorset, but even here specimens occur as individual bones and teeth. Recognising these often minute and fragmentary remains requires great skill.

Turtles and **crocodiles** are living fossils in that they have hardly changed in millions of years. The richest strata for their remains are the Portland Limestone and Purbeck Beds. Finds usually consist of isolated fragments of turtle shell or the armoured scutes (bony plates) and teeth of crocodiles, though occasional skulls have been found.

Dorset is famous for early **mammals**. The county contains one of the oldest known mammal sites in the British Isles; the Middle Jurassic rocks of West Cliff, West Bay, but the most famous sites are in the Purbeck Beds around Swanage. The first discoveries were made in the middle of the last century in a quarry high above Durlston Bay, but recent work at other sites has revealed an amazing fauna of early shrew and rodent-like mammals, together with amphibians and reptiles, including the first recorded British dinosaur egg shell. These fossils are found by bulk sampling some of the thin clay sediments associated with the limestones that contain dinosaur footprints. This amazingly detailed work illustrates the early existence of the mammals, surviving in the shadow of the dinosaurs.

INVERTEBRATES
(animals without backbones)

BRACHIOPODS

At first glance brachiopods resemble many of the bivalve sea shells found on beaches today, but in reality they are a totally unrelated and ancient form of marine life. They have existed for over 500 million years and were once the dominant shell fish of the sea, but today only a handful of species survive.

What sets brachiopods apart from modern bivalves is that they have a small hole in the shell through which a fleshy stalk protrudes, anchoring them to the sea floor. In addition, they have structures inside the shell that provide support for the soft body. Brachiopods suck water through the shell in order to filter suspended food particles.

CRUSTACEANS

Crabs and lobsters are a relatively rare group, though where they occur they may be locally common. Small Eryonid lobsters are

Goniorhynchia boueti is a typical brachiopod from the Middle Jurassic Fullers Earth Clay at Burton Bradstock.

The Cretaceous lobster *Hoploparia* from the Upper Greensand, is one of the commonest crustaceans from the rocks of Dorset.

known from the Lower Lias of Charmouth but the commonest lobsters are probably *Hoploparia* from the overlying Upper Greensand. In Purbeck, the highest beds of the Portland Limestone, the Shrimp Bed, contain the shrimp *Callianassa* that gives the rock its name.

Cardiaster latissimus, a sea urchin from Upper Greensand, Osmington Mills.

ECHINODERMS

Echinoderms are a successful group of animals that have a number of distinct features in common, a five-fold symmetry, tube feet and spiny skin. Echinoids (sea urchins) and starfish are typical, but the group also included crinoids and sea cucumbers.

Starfish are uncommon in the rocks of Dorset except at certain horizons such as the Starfish Bed, which is exposed between Eype and Seatown and contains superb specimens of the spindly brittle star *Ophioderma* (see the chapter on West Dorset for more details). Starfish have rows of tube feet that extend along the underside of each arm. Each 'foot' has a sucker on the end, with which it can stick itself to the sea floor. The tube is then contracted, so pulling the animal along. Brittle stars also use their tubed feet to filter seawater for food while their larger relatives, the starfish, are capable of pulling open sea shells, then extending their stomach into the shell in order to digest the soft parts, alive!

Echinoids, or sea urchins, are essentially starfish that have drawn the tips of their arms together in order to make a hollow, dome-shaped shell. Their tube feet protrude through rows of tiny holes that stretch from the bottom to the top of the shell, enabling them to drag themselves across the sea floor. Many echinoids protect themselves

Pentacrinites fossilis, a crinoid from the Lower Jurassic of Charmouth.

with sharp spines that extend from the shell.

The 'classic' heart-shaped sea urchin, *Micraster*, or Shepherd's Crown, is commonly found wherever the Upper Chalk is exposed in cliff sections, chalk pits and in flint rich soils, but other notable strata for sea urchins include the Cenomanian Limestone (Lower Chalk), the underlying Upper Greensand and the Osmington Oolite.

Crinoids, or 'sea lilies', are plant-like animals that have a long stalk, a cup or calyx and five finely branching arms that filter food from the sea. The stalk may be star-shaped (with five sides) or round in cross-section while the five arms are equipped with tubed feet that transport food to a mouth located at the top of the calyx, the cup housing the main soft body.

Some crinoids, such as *Pentacrinites fossilis* from Charmouth, lived on driftwood floating in the sea. Large colonies grew on the wood which finally became water-logged and sank to the sea floor, taking its doomed residents with it. Other species such as *Apiocrinus* from the Middle Jurassic Forest Marble lived attached to the sea floor.

Today only a few species of crinoid can be found alive, mostly in deep water below tropical coral reefs. However, a close relative, the feather star, can be found in profusion, especially in shallow waters along the Atlantic coast of the British Isles.

Molluscs are an incredibly diverse group of animals that include gastropods (snails and sea slugs), bivalve sea-shells and the chitons, or 'coat of mail' shells. The most advanced molluscs, the cephalopods, have a large head, well-developed eyes and are armed with tentacles. This group includes the ancient ammonites and belemnites together with the modern day nautilus, cuttlefish, octopus and squid.

Ammonites and the **Nautilus.** If there is one type of fossil that represents Dorset's palaeontological heritage it is surely the ammonite. These beautiful, spiral-shelled animals dominated the marine environment throughout the Jurassic and Cretaceous periods, finally dying out, along with the dinosaurs, during the great Cretaceous – Tertiary extinction 65 million years ago.

Ammonites vary in size and shape from the tiny one centimetre

Ammonites have a hollow, chambered shell that is often filled with crystal (in this case calcite and iron pyrites) and sediment. The many smaller chambers were filled with gas and water to produce buoyancy while the final, long chamber housed the soft body.

Because the fossil ammonite shell is so similar to the living nautilus, palaeontologists speculate that the ammonite looked like the nautilus, complete with a head, well-developed eyes and tentacles.

Promicroceras planicosta found at Charmouth to the giant *Titanites giganteus* from Portland, that may reach more than a metre in diameter. All have a hollow shell divided into many small chambers and a final large one in which the soft body was housed. The chamber walls are intricately folded where they meet the outside shell and produce a delicate pattern known as a suture line. The smaller chambers within the shell are connected together and to the body by a tube, the siphuncle. Ammonites demonstrate huge variation in shell design and ornamentation while the males and females of certain species are entirely different in appearance, often with the presumed females being much larger than the males. The nautilus in comparison has kept to the same basic shape. The most obvious external difference from ammonites is that the nautilus is fatter and broader than most ammonites while its chamber walls are saucer shaped and do not produce a complex suture line.

We can gain a good idea of what ammonites looked like by examining the living nautilus. The nautilus has a head with a pair of well-developed eyes and a ring of tentacles that extend from the open end of the shell. The bulk of the soft body is housed within the last and longest chamber while the numerous smaller chambers within the shell are filled with liquid and gas, the proportions of which can be regulated through the siphuncle, thus controlling its buoyancy. Like all cephalopods, including squid, cuttlefish and octopus, the nautilus can squirt a jet of water through a tube within the head, allowing it to swim through the sea by jet propulsion. Unlike other living cephalopods, the nautilus does not have an ink sac.

Belemnites are the commonest fossil in Dorset's marine Jurassic rocks and are usually the first fossil that people find on the beaches, particularly of West Dorset. In the past they were known as 'thunderbolts' and 'devils bullets' and were believed to fall from the sky during lightning storms. In reality these pencil-shaped fossils are the internal shells of a squid-like creature. Like ammonites, belemnites had a hollow, chambered section within the shell that contained gas and fluid to produce and control buoyancy. The head was well-developed with eyes, tentacles and an ink sac.

Cuttlefish are also known from the Jurassic rocks of Dorset, particularly from the Lower Jurassic around Charmouth and the Upper Jurassic Kimmeridge Clay. At both sites specimens can be found complete with skin, tentacles and ink sac.

Gastropods are snails of which many thousands of species flourish today in a variety of habitats, in the sea, fresh water and on land. The successful evolution of gastropods is recorded in Dorset's rocks. In the Lower Jurassic, they are relatively rare but include the highly decorative *Pleurotomaria*. In the Portland Limestone the high-spired *Aptyxiella portlandica* is common in the shelly Roach Stone. In the Tertiary Barton Beds, gastropods dominate the fossil fauna and numerous highly advanced species evolved into forms that are virtually identical to modern-day species.

Bivalves. Most modern sea shells, such as clams, mussels and oysters, belong to a group of molluscs known as the bivalves, characterized by having two shells united by a hinge. In geological terms the bivalves are a relatively ancient group, but the Jurassic

The pencil-shaped shells of Belemnites are locally abundant, particularly around Seatown and Charmouth in West Dorset. These shells provided the internal support for a soft body similar to that of a modern-day cuttlefish.

Gastropods are snails, the majority of which are almost identical to this 160 million year old *Bathrotomaria* from the Upper Jurassic Corallian rocks at Black Head, east of Weymouth.

marked a time of great expansion. Many of the sea shells that we are familiar with today had already evolved by the early Jurassic, including the scallop *Pseudopecten*, whose fossil shells can be seen in the sandy rocks on the beaches below Thornecombe Beacon. One spectacular deposit of bivalves in Dorset comprises the countless oysters that form the Cinder Bed at Lulworth, Worbarrow Bay and Durlston Bay. Some bivalves developed into bizarre forms, the most notable being the oyster *Gryphaea*, otherwise known as the 'Devil's toe nail', which occurs in the oldest Jurassic rocks at Lyme Regis.

Tubeworms are another successful group that can be found as fossils throughout the rocks of Dorset and yet continue to flourish on rocky shores today. Because they secrete a hard, white calcium shell, they are robust and easily fossilised. Large clusters of small round tubeworms can be found within the Upper Greensand, but perhaps the most spectacular species is *Serpula intestinalis*, which can be collected from the Oxford Clay at Jordan Cliff near Preston, Weymouth. Tubeworms also form a component of the patch reefs within the Portland Limestone. Some tubeworms encrust or grow on other shells, including brachiopods.

Corals are not particularly common in the rocks of the county, despite the Upper Jurassic Corallian Beds taking their name from fossilised corals. Corals grow in two basic forms, as colonies or solitary individuals. Solitary corals can be found within the Ringstead Coral Bed and the Cenomanian Limestone (Lower Chalk).

Bryozoans or sea mats are colonial animals that create a pattern of minute cells that encrust hard surfaces such as shells. They are particularly obvious in the Inferior Oolite.

Sponges are simple, funnel-shaped animals with a porous skeleton composed of tiny interlocking needles of silica or calcite. Many of the flints found within the Chalk have developed around sponges, while flint itself is composed of silica, which may in part be derived from sponges and is carried in solution through the rocks. The Sponge Bed within the Middle Jurassic Inferior Oolite consists almost entirely of well-preserved sponges whose honeycomb texture is distinctive.

Trace fossils are tracks or marks made by animals when the rocks were being deposited. To be fossilised, the sediments have to be soft

Trace fossils are the tracks and burrows made by animals such as worms, crustaceans and even dinosaurs that burrow through or walk over the soft sediments. These *Thalassinoides* burrows from the Lower Lias of Lyme Regis are thought to have been made by a crustacean.

enough to allow the formation of the features which then have to be buried without being damaged or destroyed. Therefore most trace fossils form in areas where soft mud or sand accumulated in calm or settled water.

The most common trace fossils are the tracks or burrows made by worms and crustaceans such as lobsters. Many trace fossils are quite distinctive and even if palaeontologists do not know which animal has made them, they are still given scientific names. A fine example is the looped pattern called *Phycosyphon* from the Starfish Bed at Eype, which was probably made by an animal moving back and forth across the sea floor, filtering the sand as it went.

Tool marks are sedimentary structures rather than trace fossils, as they are created by dead animals or plants being bounced or dragged across the sea floor by currents: a good example can be found in the Starfish Bed, where starfish have been washed across the sand leaving resting traces and drag marks.

Without a doubt, the most spectacular trace fossils are those made by dinosaurs. Dorset has more than its fair share of footprints and trackways, and the Purbeck Beds of Durlston Bay and the small quarries in the area are the best place to see such features, a number of which, such as the trackways at Sunnydown Farm and Keats Quarry, have been preserved. Most footprints were made by the three-toed *Iguanadon* and *Megalosaurus*, but those at Keats Quarry were created by a number of large four-legged sauropod dinosaurs, and are much rarer.

MICROFOSSILS

As the name suggests, microfossils are minute (usually under one millimetre) and are essentially fossilised plankton whose beautiful range of forms is only visible under the microscope. The commonest and most useful to a palaeontologist are ostracods, which resemble minute potatoes, and foramanifera, the shape of whose tiny shells are amazingly diverse.

Within certain sediments microfossils can be widespread, but collecting them requires a specialised technique. Essentially they are collected by bulk sampling, scooping up several kilos of sediment and sieving in a laboratory using a variety of techniques. The actual fossil hunting takes place under the binocular microscope, where the fossils are carefully plucked from the residue of sand grains and other material.

PLANTS

Fossilised wood is common throughout most of the Jurassic and early Cretaceous rocks, indicating that land was nearby even when Dorset lay submerged beneath the sea. Within the thick clay sequences of the Lower Lias and the Kimmeridge clay, wood is often preserved as hard black lumps of lignite that may occasionally retain some of the original wood texture.

The most spectacular plant remains come from the Fossil Forests at Lulworth and on Portland. Here, an entire forest has been preserved together with the soil in which the trees grew. The forest became preserved as a result of the growth of a single-celled green algae that

A fossil tree outside the Portland Heights Hotel. Numerous pieces of fossil wood can be seen in walls and gardens across Portland and most is found lying within the dirt beds or fossilised soils at the base of the Purbeck Beds.

flourished in a shallow hypersaline lagoon that flooded the forest. In places these algae have grown into dome-shaped structures known as algal stromatolites. These are among the most primitive forms of life known on the planet; some of the earliest stromatolites are over 3,000 million years old.

RESPONSIBLE AND SAFE COLLECTING

Fossils don't have to be collected to be enjoyed. This book is as much about the 'geological language' that allows us to understand and appreciate the story fossils tell us about Dorset's ancient past as it is about providing a guide to collecting.

It is important to remember that there are many sites where fossil collecting *en masse* is entirely unsuitable, including those that experience little or no erosion and inland exposures such as disused quarries. Furthermore, as a general rule, fossils belong to the owners of the land, whose permission to collect is necessary at many sites. There are, however, sites where they can readily be collected, especially where rapid natural erosion increases the likelihood of their being destroyed. West Dorset's beaches are ideal, but it is crucial that collectors act safely and responsibly in order to conserve the sites and retain the scientific importance associated with the fossils.

THE COAST

All beaches and cliffs are prone to the natural hazards of cliff falls, tides and, in certain areas, landslides and mudflows. It is absolutely essential that collectors observe local warning information signs, restrict their activity to the beaches only, keep a watchful eye on the cliffs and mudflows and check the tides. A hard hat will offer a certain amount of protection from falling rocks, and highly visible clothing is always sensible if working on an isolated section of the coast.

The best time to go collecting is immediately after a winter storm, as this is when erosion is at its greatest and more fossils are likely to be uncovered. Extreme caution is required, as landslides and rough

The best place to collect fossils at Charmouth is where the sea has washed away the mud on the beach.

seas are much more likely at this time of year. Cliff falls are a constant hazard throughout the year, stay away from the cliffs at all times.

Contrary to popular belief, a hammer is not an essential tool for finding fossils. Around Charmouth and Lyme Regis fossils can be picked up loose on the beaches where they have been eroded from the mudflows by the sea. In other areas fossils such as dinosaur footprints are often too large to be collected and should be left for others to enjoy. Some fossils do need to be chipped from the rocks in order to be collected, but using a hammer successfully and knowing what is worth breaking is a skill that only comes with practice. It is essential to use a hardened, geological hammer (ordinary hammers may splinter and break) and wear safety glasses. You should keep others at a safe distance. Do not hammer indiscriminately or at the cliffs, for not only is such an activity clearly dangerous, it can result in unsightly damage and some landowners object to such activity on their land. Besides, the vast majority of fossils within the soft clay

If you use a hammer, make sure that it is a hardened, geological hammer, and wear safety goggles to protect your eyes.

cliffs such as at Kimmeridge and Charmouth are crushed flat and will simply crumble away.

On the West Dorset coast the displays and wardens at the Charmouth Heritage Coast Centre offers informed local advice regarding fossil collecting. The Centre and a number of museums and fossil shops in Lyme Regis run guided fossil collecting walks – always the best way to get started. There is also a voluntary fossil collecting code of conduct for the West Dorset coast, details of which are available at the Charmouth Heritage Coast Centre.

INLAND

Most inland sites are exposed to very limited rates of erosion. Working quarries are the exception, but such places are clearly dangerous and subject to rigorous health and safety laws. It is essential that collectors seek permission to collect in any site and follow the advice provided by quarry managers. Health and Safety Legislation requires the use of hard hats and high visibility jackets in active sites.

SCIENTIFICALLY IMPORTANT FINDS

One of the exciting aspects of fossil collecting is that there is always the prospect of discovering something new to science. Recognising the importance of such a find is essential and collectors should spend time acquainting themselves with the types of fossils they are liable to find at any given site. Useful books and pamphlets are listed in 'Further Reading'.

From a scientific point of view fossils are of little value if the location and the strata they came from are unknown, and this is especially true of rare or unique specimens. It is essential to record as much information about your finds as you can.

LOOKING AFTER YOUR FOSSILS

While on the beach, carry newspaper and plastic bags in which to wrap your finds. Some fossils require cleaning or preparation in order to remove the surrounding rock and this can involve great skill, which is only gained with time, practice and the correct tools. Sharp stone chisels, small hammers and air-powered engraving tools are best. Obviously, if you have been lucky enough to find a really well-preserved ammonite, fish or ichthyosaur and have never cleaned fossils before DON'T start on these specimens! Preparation is best left to the experts, and advice can be gained from local museums and fossil shops.

If you do want to build a major collection and are hoping to find something new to science, don't expect it to happen overnight. Fossil collecting depends upon natural skill, a great deal of patience and more than just a little luck. For many of the best collectors this is a life-long and all-consuming interest. Finally don't hoard your collection but share it with others. Organisations such as the Dorset Geologists Association meet regularly and occasionally hold public events where you can display your collection.

THE STORY OF MARY ANNING

Mary Anning was born in Lyme Regis in 1799 and remains one of the most famous fossil collectors of all. She was the first to extract a complete ichthyosaur from the local area and had an exceptional relationship with the gentlemen scholars of the day in an age when the development of scientific theory was very much a male preoccupation. What is perhaps most extraordinary about Mary is that her reputation has endured whilst the many other collectors of the time languish in relative obscurity.

Mary learnt the skills of collecting from her father, Richard, who supplemented the family's income through the sale of fossil 'curiosities' to passing tourists. When he died in 1810, Mary and her brother Joseph continued to collect, although there still remains some uncertainty regarding the role of their mother, who was also called Mary and collected fossils. In 1811, Mary and Joseph found and extracted the first complete fossil ichthyosaur or 'sea dragon'. Mary went on to discover and extract the first complete plesiosaur, the finest specimens of a rare ray and the even rarer flying reptile, *Dimorphodon*.

What sets Mary apart from many of her contemporaries was her awareness that fossils were more than simple 'curiosities'. A significant factor was her friendship with the Philpot sisters who had an interest in fossils and came to Lyme on a regular basis. They in turn were visited by the eminent scientists of the day. As a result, and despite her humble background, Mary discussed her finds and theories with scientists such as the Rev. William Buckland and Henry De la Beche, whose collaborative early work on the affinities and morphology of the ichthyosaur were of ground-breaking importance. Henry De la Beche lived in Lyme and it may be that Mary encouraged his interest in fossils. He later became the first director of the Geological Survey of Great Britain, while William Buckland

Mary Anning, 1799-1847.

became the first professor of Geology at Oxford. Heady circles for a local girl!

Collecting did have its rewards; Mary's first ichthyosaur was sold for £23, then a considerable sum. A few years later it sold at auction for twice as much and it is now one of the most prized specimens of the Natural History Museum in London, where it can be seen on display.

Mary died in 1847 and is buried in St Michael's parish church in Lyme Regis, just yards from the cliffs and beaches upon which she made such important discoveries. A stained glass window commemorates her achievements, while it is popularly thought that the tongue-twisting phrase '*she sells sea shells by the sea shore*' can be attributed to this exceptional woman.

Today a number of local professional collectors follow in Mary Anning's footsteps. Some are in communication with leading experts around the world, while others are content to simply keep or sell their fossils. However, all have an important role to play, for it is the local experts, professional and amateur, whose patient search of the beaches lead to many important new finds every year. Without their effort many unique and rare specimens would be lost to the ravages of the sea.

THE WEST DORSET COAST

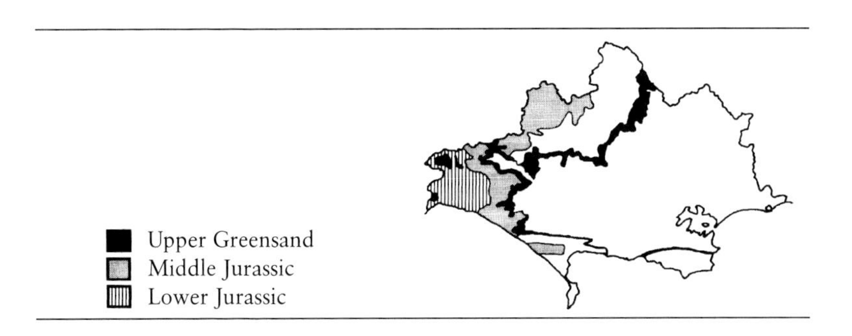

The West Dorset coast is without doubt the best place to find fossils in the county. There are lots to be found on the beaches, many are superbly preserved and some are preserved in remarkable ways.

The dark clay and limestone rocks exposed in the lower cliffs around Lyme Regis and Charmouth are known as the Lower Lias and, at around 200 million years old, they are the earliest Jurassic sediments. The cliff tops are capped by younger rocks of Cretaceous age, the Upper Greensand, that are only about 100 million years old and lie on the eroded surface of the Jurassic rocks. It is this sandstone that gives the golden capping to cliffs such as Golden Cap and causes the many landslides that have played such an important role in fashioning the character of this stretch of coast. Inland, the Lower Lias rocks are poorly exposed due to their soft nature and give rise to the rolling countryside of the Marshwood Vale.

The Lower Lias formed in a muddy tropical sea that was packed with marine life. Spiral-shelled ammonites and squid-like belemnites are the commonest fossils found, but beautiful sea lilies or crinoids (plant-like animals) and trace fossils are also typical. The bones of ichthyosaurs are not uncommon though complete skeletons are rare. Some of the most unusual fossils are those of insects such as

Golden Cap from Charmouth. Here the dark Lower Jurassic rocks can be seen dipping down towards the east while they are capped by Cretaceous aged Upper Greensand.

dragonflies, beetles and flies. Perhaps the most important fossil is that of *Scelidosaurus*, a dinosaur known from a handful of specimens only and possibly unique to Charmouth (recent discoveries in the Inner Hebrides of Scotland may be *Scelidosaurus*). These creatures, along with prolific amounts of wood, were washed into the sea and provide geologists with a glimpse of a real 'Jurassic Park'.

Further along the coast, between Seatown and Eype, younger rocks of the Middle Lias form cliffs which are distinctly sandy in nature. This is the result of the shallowing of the Jurassic sea and gives rise to different fossil communities here. They include bivalve shells such as scallops and numerous, well-preserved brachiopods. The most famous rock layer is the Starfish Bed that contains superbly preserved fossil brittle stars. To find it, look for the massive boulders on the beach with a flat surface. Many boast square holes where specimens have been collected, but you may also see fragments of starfish – and perhaps even a complete one.

Other features of particular interest are limestone boulders that contain numerous pebbles riddled with fossilised borings. These

Dense populations of brittle starfish are occasionally found on the beaches below Thornecombe Beacon, between Seatown and Eype. They are not from the famous Starfish Bed but probably formed in similar conditions.

pebbles must have been eroded shortly after the rocks formed and were then re-deposited at a later date. The most spectacular of these deposits is the Junction Bed, a metre thick band of creamy pink limestone packed with eroded or encrusted fossils, particularly ammonites. This stratum represents over three million years of geological time during the Upper Lias. It is a 'condensed sequence', a thin band of rock representing a long period of time and formed in a shallow sea subject to periods of both slow deposition and erosion.

The beach between Seatown and Eype is extremely rough and boulder strewn, while the cliffs are prone to sudden cliff falls and may exude soft mudflows and quicksands, especially during or shortly after wet weather.

At West Bay, the towering orange cliffs are dominated by Bridport Sands capped by rocks of Middle Jurassic age, the Inferior Oolite – a limestone that formed in shallow tropical waters. Because of the shallow environment, the stratigraphy of the Inferior Oolite is complex, as numerous layers, represented by zones of geological time, are missing at different places due to erosion or non deposition as the

The very youngest Lower Jurassic rocks, the Bridport Sands, form the striking cliffs between Burton Bradstock and West Bay. Cliff falls are a constant hazard while in the distance can be seen the dark clays that form the cliffs of West Dorset.

A block of highly fossiliferous Middle Jurassic Inferior Oolite limestone from the beach at Burton Bradstock, complete with ammonites, belemnites, bivalves and brachiopods.

Black Ven landslide with Lyme Regis in the background. The two arcs of boulders on the beach mark the extent of the 1958/9 landslip and provide an indication of the enormous amount of erosion that takes place here.

shifting oolitic sands were forming. The rock is at its thickest in Dorset to the north of the county around Sherborne, where it was once extensively quarried for building stone.

The Inferior Oolite contains a superb range of fossils including ammonites, shells such as brachiopods, bivalves and snails, together with sponges and bryozoans, all of which can be seen in the large fallen blocks on the beach. Fossil collecting between West Bay and Burton Bradstock is not recommended as the cliffs are unstable and there is always the chance of falling rock and the occasional catastrophic cliff collapse.

Erosion rates along the West Dorset coast can exceed one metre a year and are the reason why so many fossils continue to be found on the beaches, especially after winter storms. Landslides create a distinctive undercliff, an area of mudslides between the sea cliff and high inland cliff. The fossil rich Lower Jurassic clay rocks that form the sea cliffs are capped by the Upper Greensand that form the high inland cliffs. Rainwater seeps through the sandstone but it cannot pass through the clay. After periods of heavy rain the underlying clay surface deep within the cliff becomes lubricated, allowing the cliff-top sands to slide into the undercliff. The slipped material and rain-water also causes the softer Jurassic rocks to slip, resulting in large mudslides that may spill across the beach and into the sea. As the sea washes away the soft mud it uncovers thousands of fossils that can be picked off the beaches, even by the most amateur of collectors.

Many of the fossils found in West Dorset are beautifully preserved and quite distinctive to the area. After burial most are crushed flat within the soft clay rocks that form the bulk of the cliffs. However, crystals can fill hollow shells and in the Lower Jurassic rocks around Lyme Regis and Charmouth these usually take the form of colourful calcite or iron pyrites (fool's gold), adding to their attraction.

Most of the Lower Lias rocks are rich in calcite, a mineral carried in solution by water percolating through the rocks when they were buried deep under ground. As a result some of the clay layers became cemented together to form hard bands of limestone or layers of nodules, beds of rock containing distinctive round lenses of limestone. Any cavity in these rocks became filled with calcite crystal and these now form veins of white crystal seen in the grey limestone boulders on the beaches.

Within some of the limestone rocks, hollow ammonite shells also became filled with calcite crystals that vary in colour from white to green and a deep reddish brown. When extracted from the rock these specimens are translucent and the chamber walls and delicate suture lines can be seen. The Green Ammonite Beds that run through the cliffs of Stonebarrow, east of Charmouth, owe their name to the green calcite that fills the ammonites found in certain nodule horizons within it. The fossils found within these rocks are extremely difficult to clean, while the green calcite is only visible when the ammonite is broken open or sectioned by a rock saw.

Iron pyrites is composed of iron and sulphur and forms in association with bacteria under stagnant conditions where there is no oxygen. Such conditions existed when many of the dark clay rocks of the Lower Lias were forming. As a result a bacterial sludge of iron and sulphur filled the hollow shells of ammonites. Later, this sludge crystallised into bright and shiny fool's gold, forming a perfect

An ammonite, *Promicroceras*, whose beautiful opalescence is due to minute layers of fossilised mother-of-pearl within the shell.

internal cast of the ammonite shell. These beautiful fossils are washed from the clay rocks onto the beaches, to be picked up with no tools other than a good pair of eyes.

Despite the fine preservation of fossils by fool's gold, a problem lies ahead for those who collect fossils cast in this iron-rich mineral. For millions of years the fossils lay trapped in the rocks. Once exposed to the air, the mineral starts to decay. The bright golden shine can rapidly tarnish and some specimens actually fall apart after just a few years exposed to the atmosphere. To prevent this process, soak the fossils in fresh water when first found and store them in a dry place. Pyrite decay, as it is known, also produces acids that can react with other fossils, so it is best to keep individual specimens apart lest they all decompose.

Rocks that form in stagnant conditions are distinctive in that they consist of black, laminated shales that are undisturbed by bottom-dwelling creatures such as shrimps or worms. They usually contain pyrite crystals and are often bituminous, that is, they contain oil or gas. Under such extreme conditions, fish or ichthyosaurs that die and sink to the sea floor are fossilised without being torn apart and eaten by scavengers. Thus their skeletons are buried undisturbed, resulting

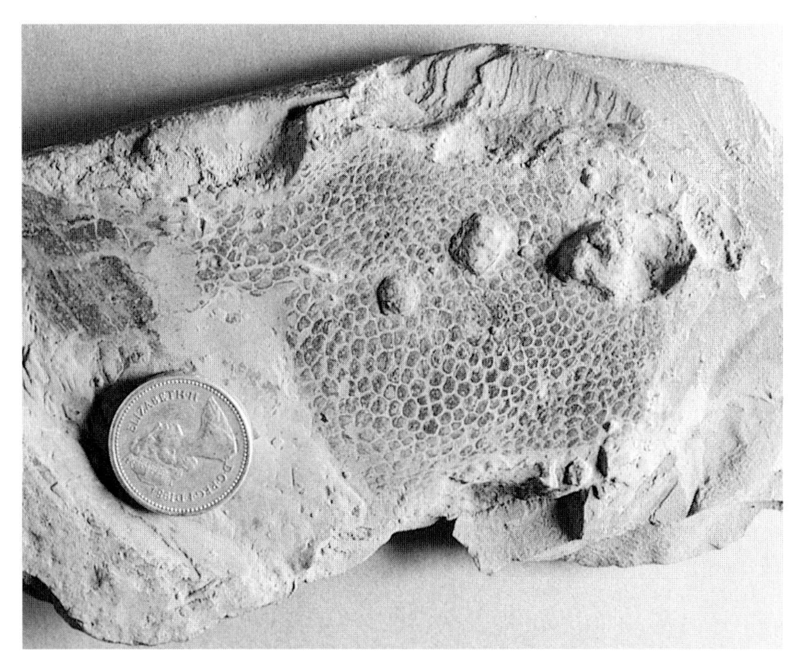

One of the rarest finds in the Charmouth area, this is skin from the dinosaur *Scelidosaurus.*

in superb preservation. Indeed, some specimens are so well-preserved that a near forensic examination can be undertaken on them. For instance, it is not uncommon to find ichthyosaurs with their heads arched back, perhaps due to the muscles contracting during rigor-mortis.

However, fossilisation in stagnant environments can produce even more startling results, especially if combined with rapid burial. Sometimes the process of decay was slowed long enough for the soft parts of animals to become preserved, allowing an even greater insight into ancient fossil life. Perhaps the most important single soft part specimen yet discovered was dinosaur skin found in the winter of 1985. The specimen consisted of a partial skeleton of the dinosaur *Scelidosaurus*, uncovered in a cliff fall on Stonebarrow Beach, east of Charmouth. Two patches of skin were found, showing such details as different sized scales.

Other outstanding finds of recent years include the rear half of an

A perfectly preserved dragonfly; the Lower Jurassic rocks of Charmouth are famous for the exceptional fauna of fossil insects that they contain.

ichthyosaur complete with the skin showing both flukes of the tail. In the past, Victorian palaeontologists believed that ichthyosaurs had a crocodile-shaped tail, but similar soft part specimens from Germany have shown that they had a vertical tail with two flukes, rather like a shark.

Charmouth is particularly famous for exquisitely preserved insects within some of the fine grained limestone rocks. Flies, beetles, dragonflies and even grasshoppers have been found. Some specimens are easily recognised but others require an effort of imagination to visualise and are not surprisingly, the subject of considerable debate. These fossils from Charmouth represent quite possibly the finest insect fauna from the Lower Jurassic anywhere in the world.

Portland Bill. The Island is dominated by quarrying for Portland Limestone. Older workings such as those in the foreground create a distinctive character and provide a unique environment rich in geology, stone heritage and wildlife.

PORTLAND

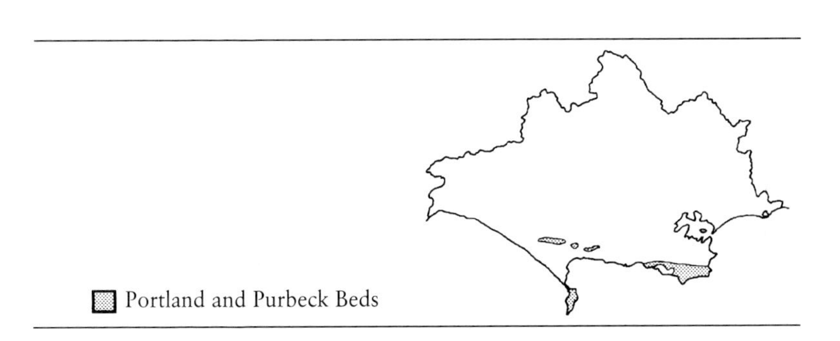

The Isle of Portland is formed from the youngest Jurassic age rocks, the 135 million-year-old Portland Limestone and Lower Purbeck Beds. These rocks, and the fossils they contain, tell a fascinating story that illustrates the sudden shift from sedimentation under the Jurassic Sea to the formation of land on which soils developed and a forest grew.

The Island is dominated by quarrying for Portland Stone, perhaps the most famous building stone in Britain, if not the world. It is composed from a sandwich of rocks capped by the Portland Limestone, and Purbeck Beds and underlain by the Portland Sands and Kimmeridge Clay. These rocks are tilted to the south and east, creating the distinctive wedge shape of the Island with its towering limestone cliffs to the north dipping gently to sea level at Portland Bill. The huge natural expanse of Portland Harbour has been created from the erosion of the Kimmeridge Clay.

The Portland Limestone is divided into two layers, the underlying Cherty Series consisting of about 20 metres of limestone with bands of chert, a hard flinty material, overlain by up to 5 metres of the Freestone Series. The rocks formed in a shallow tropical sea similar to areas of the Caribbean today. Minute grains of sand and shell fragments were rolled across the sea floor, accumulating layer upon layer of calcium and creating tiny egg-shaped structures known as ooliths. The result is an oolitic limestone composed of countless millions of these minute spheres. Because the rock contains the same structure in every direction, it can be cut or sculpted in any direction. This quality, coupled with colour, texture, hardness and durability, makes the Freestone Series of the Portland Limestone such a fine building stone.

In terms of fossils, the Portland Limestone is the most important source of marine reptiles from this particular period within the Late Jurassic anywhere in the world. This does not mean that ichthyosaurs, plesiosaurs and turtles are regularly discovered in the quarries, for they remain incredibly rare. The truth is that few other sites of the same age contain marine reptiles and therefore Portland, despite the low frequency of finds, is important. Specimens are displayed in the County Museum, Dorchester, and the Portland Museum at Wakeham. Sadly, few specimens have been recovered in recent years, but this is probably a reflection on changes in working techniques from quarrying by hand to mechanisation.

Fossil reptiles may be rare within the Portland Limestone but shells are not. The Basal Shell Bed at the bottom of the Cherty Series, and the Roach Stone at the top of the freestones, are packed with bivalve shells. In the Roach the fossils are typically preserved as casts where the shell itself has been dissolved away to leave a mould of the inside of the shell and a cast of the exterior. The casts often preserve the decoration of the shell while the moulds display features such as muscle scars and the hinge structures where the two shells slotted together. The quarrymen of old gave these fossils the name 'osses 'eds', as, when held at a certain orientation, and with a bit of imagination, they bear an uncanny resemblance to a horse's head. The high-spired snail shell *Aptyxiella portlandica* is also preserved in the same way, and is locally known as the 'Portland screw'.

The Portland Limestone also contains the huge ammonite, *Titanites giganteus*. They can reach over a metre in diameter and numerous specimens can be seen in walls and gardens across the Island. Also occurring in the Freestone beds are patch reefs, accumulations of shells, tubeworms and distinctly banded algae

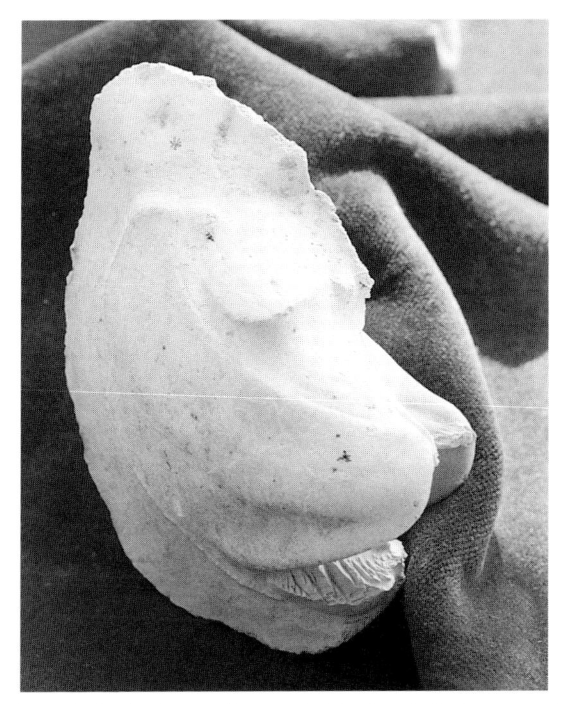

An 'Osses 'ed', the internal cast of a bivalve shell that resembles a 'horses head', the name provided by the quarrymen of the Island.

A Portland Screw, *Aptyxiella portlandica*, is the internal cast of a high-spired snail shell that is common in the Roach Stone, especially in the north of the Island.

that once stood on the sea floor among the shifting oolitic sands.

The Roach is the last fully marine rock of Jurassic age to be deposited in Dorset. Lying directly above it are fossilised soils, an ancient forest and limestone rocks that formed in association with algae that grew in brackish swamps and lagoons. The rocks that formed in these conditions are known as the Purbeck Beds and include a thick and varied sequence of clays and limestones which on Portland reach their maximum thickness around the centre of the Island.

The oldest Purbeck Beds consist of two thin soils developed within a massive limestone known as the Hard Cap. The limestone contains the hollow casts of trees and branches surrounded by algal growths. It appears that sea levels dropped to expose the recently deposited Portland Limestone. Once land had emerged, soils formed and an exotic woodland including monkey-puzzle trees and cycad ferns ultimately followed. A short time later this low-lying forest was drowned by swamps or lagoons in which the trees initially remained upright, allowing algae to grow around them. The algae trapped fine calcium-rich mud as it grew outward from the wood, creating a circular ring of porous limestone. Eventually the trees fell over and the algae continued to grow on the topside of the formation. Between these structures occur fine laminated algae that makes up the remainder of the rock.

The finest development of both soils and fossilised wood are to be seen in the overlying Great Dirt Bed and the famous Fossil Forest. The soil is a distinctive feature across the Island in that it forms an indented ledge underneath the prominent Soft Cap or Fossil Forest. Just like the modern soils of Portland, the Great Dirt Bed comprises limestone pebbles within a dark soil matrix. Most of the fossil wood now visible in gardens and walls, such as the Portland Heights Hotel and the Portland Museum, has been found within this strata. Where the trees remained upright, they form the Fossil Forest. Just as with the underlying beds, the forest was inundated by brackish conditions in which algae flourished. The algae grew across the floor of the swamp and around the base of the trees, which eventually collapsed leaving round doughnut shaped structures with a hole in the middle where the tree used to be. These structures are known as burs and

The Fossil Forest, Kingbarrow Quarry. All that is left of the trees is a circular bur of algae that grew around the base of the tree once it became submerged in a shallow swamp.

some still contain fossilised wood. Analysis of the wood in cross-section shows that the annual growth rings are irregular in thickness, suggesting that the trees grew in a seasonal climate and experienced prolonged wet and dry conditions.

Huge areas of the Fossil Forest have been quarried away, but one of the finest remaining exposures can be seen in the western corner of Kingbarrow Quarry, just behind the old lime kiln, about three hundred metres along the road from the Portland Heights Hotel towards Easton (Grid Ref: SY691728).

Because Portland's rocks formed in shallow seas or swamps and lagoons there is a great deal of lateral variation in the geology. This means that no one locality displays all the geological and fossil features of interest. This is nowhere more evident than with the distribution of the Fossil Forest, which is best developed in the north of the Island and generally disappears to the south. This change can be seen in the quarries along the east coast between Southwell and Portland Bill. Follow the coast path from Freshwater Bay (Grid Ref: SY691704) and you will see a typical exposure of the Portland Limestone, Cap, Great Dirt Bed and Fossil Forest. However, within four hundred metres of the road the solid limestone strata of the Fossil Forest gives way to a finely laminated limestone that contains dome-shaped structures. These are algal stromatolites, and they are among the most ancient forms of life in the fossil record. Below the stromatolites, the fossil soils have been reworked by erosion, suggesting that a channel or lagoon existed at or near this point.

Above the caps lie a series of thin, slabby limestone rocks interspersed with beds of clay. These are well displayed within Coombefield Quarry just north of Southwell, though they are only accessible with prior permission from the quarry operators. One of the finest features within these beds are fossilised ripple marks that are superbly exposed at the top of the West Weare cliffs south of Blacknor (Grid Ref: SY680713) and in nearby quarries. As with all other Purbeck Beds on the Island, these rocks formed in lagoons subject to intense evaporation. When the water level dropped, ripple marks developed, just as they do in shallow waters today. Evaporation caused the muds to crack open and allowed salt crystals to develop, both of which have been fossilised.

Such conditions are ideal for the preservation of dinosaur footprints, as is the case in Purbeck, all be it in slightly younger strata. Curiously, only one footprint has been discovered in the rocks on Portland for reasons that still puzzle geologists. Occasional fossil fish, turtle bones and even insects are to be found in the thin limestones, but they are neither common nor intact.

INLAND EXPOSURES

A number of old quarries around the Weymouth area display the Portland Limestone and Lower Purbeck Beds, from Portesham Quarry (a Regionally Important Geological Geomorphological Site, RIGS) (Grid Ref: SY611859), to Chalbury Hill (a Site of Special Scientific Interest) (Grid Ref: SY693837, and on to Poxwell Quarry (RIGS) (Grid Ref: SY744835). All are well worth a visit, though prior

Portesham Quarry and the view over the Weymouth Anticline to Portland in the distance. The Portland Limestone and Lower Purbeck Beds are exposed in the quarry and can be seen forming a ridge that runs away to the north of Weymouth. The valley below is formed from the soft Kimmeridge Clay.

permission is required for the latter. (Contact the Dorset Important Geological/Geomorphological Sites Group for details: see Further Reading.)

The largest difference between the exposure inland and those on Portland is that the limestone is no longer oolitic but is instead a fine white calcium mud rather like chalk. The overlying Dirt Beds are generally less well-developed but fossilised trees, still standing upright, can be seen at some of these sites. Portesham Quarry contains a six-feet long fallen log covered by algal material. Obviously fossil collecting is not appropriate at these quarry sites.

WEYMOUTH, OSMINGTON AND RINGSTEAD

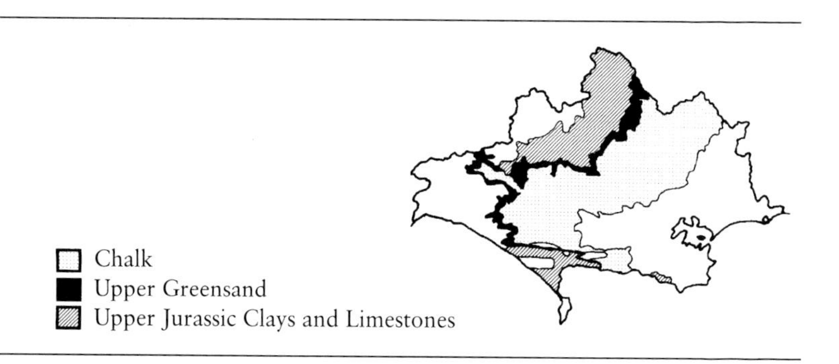

Weymouth lies at the centre of a huge dome of rocks known as the Weymouth Anticline. To the south the rocks dip gently to form the wedge-shaped Isle of Portland. To the north the hard Portland Limestone plunges into the ground, forming a prominent ridge from Portesham in the west, then eastwards through Chalbury Hill and Poxwell before emerging in the cliffs of Ringstead Bay. Between these exposures of Portland Limestone successive layers of rock outcrop like the concentric rings of an onion through the shores of the Fleet and Portland Harbour to Osmington and Ringstead Bay. Inland, the hard and soft strata create a series of ridges and vales that run parallel to the coast and can be seen from Portesham Quarry.

The Oxford Clay is the oldest of these rocks and, like most soft strata, it is poorly exposed in Dorset, tending to form the vales between hills. On the coast the Oxford Clay is only seen at Tidmoor Point on the Fleet and at Jordan Cliff, which lies at the end of Preston beach, east of Weymouth. Tidmoor Point is known for its ammonites, but the low erosion rates and wildlife importance of the Fleet makes it an unsuitable place to collect them.

Some specimens of *Gryphaea diladata* from the Oxford Clay at Jordan Cliff demonstrate the extraordinary feature of xenomorphism. These oysters settle on hard surfaces such as ammonite shells and take on the exact form of that shell as they grow. The result, an oyster that looks like an ammonite.

Jordan Cliff is one of the most important sites in the British Isles for marine reptiles from the Oxford Clay but, as with the Portland Limestone, they are extremely rare. The importance of the site is more a reflection on the scarcity of Oxford Clay exposures across the country than the volume of finds. However, the mudflows and landslides do yield numerous large *Gryphaea dilatata* shells that demonstrate a fascinating feature of oysters, xenomorphism. Oysters such as *Gryphaea* start life attached to a hard substrate and only as they mature do they become unattached and sit on the sea floor. During the attached phase, the oyster shell develops as an exact copy of the substrate it is growing on. In some cases, that surface was the dead shell of an ammonite and as a result some xenomorphic *Gryphaea* contain a perfect copy of the ammonite shell they once knew as 'home'.

Above the Oxford Clay lies a striking and complex series of limestones, sandstones and clays known as the Corallian Beds. These are exposed on the shores of the Fleet, just east of the Narrows and on the beaches and cliffs either side of Osmington. To the west

The Osmington Oolite strata march across the shore at low tide. These rocks were deposited in shallow waters and contain a wealth of fossils and sedimentary structures.

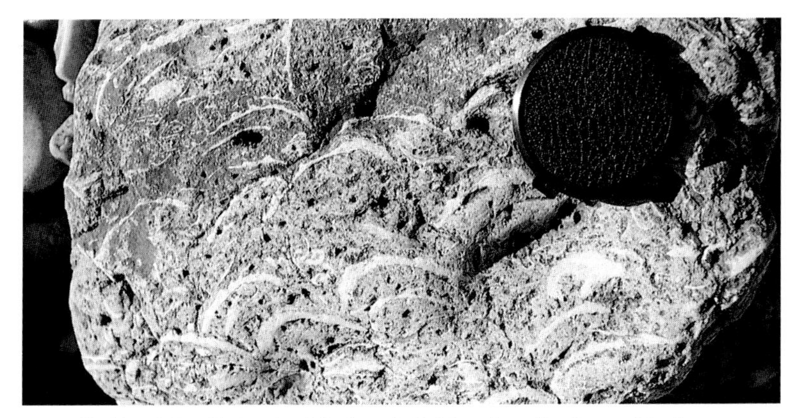

Shells of the distinctive bivalve shell *Myophorella*, lie upside down within the Osmington Oolite at Bran Point, indicating that the rocks were deposited in a strong current.

of Osmington Mills the rocks have been tilted into a near vertical position and hard bands of limestone known as the Osmington Oolite march across the foreshore at low tide. To the east, the rocks gently dip down to sea level, providing a good exposure through the entire sequence.

As with most oolitic limestones, the Osmington Oolite contains a great wealth of fossils dominated by a spectacular number of shells, particularly of the species *Myophorella*, a distinct and decorative bivalve. Some rocks on the beach, namely the Trigonia Bed, are packed with shells that nearly all lie the same way up. When sea shells are deposited in a strong current, the shells are more stable with the convex surface uppermost, indicating that the Trigonia Bed was deposited under such conditions. Other evidence of strong currents can be seen in blocks of ripple-bedded sandstone on the beach and striking cross-bedding, especially within the large round sandstone boulders known as 'doggers' that can be seen on the beach.

The small sea urchin, *Nucleolites*, gastropods, occasional ammonites and large numbers of trace fossils typify these strata and examples can be found in the fallen blocks on the beach between Osmington and Ringstead Bay. At the headland of Bran Point, one limestone band contains a spectacular number of the U-shaped worm burrow, *Arenicolites*, that can be seen cutting through the rocks. Identical burrows are made by ragworms in the sands beneath shallow, tidal waters today.

Once in Ringstead Bay, the geology changes from shallow water limestones to deeper water clay, initially the Ringstead Waxy Clays followed by the Ringstead Coral Bed, which has, for the time being been obscured by coast defence works. The bed is unique to this area of the coast and contains a rich fauna that includes corals, ammonites and crustaceans. Above the Coral Bed, lies the Kimmeridge Clay, which is the single thickest geological rock formation in the county. The lowest clays are packed with the large oyster shell *Deltoideum delta* and contain the distinctive brachiopod *Torquirhynchia inconstans*. Elsewhere in Dorset, the same strata are completely different, the result of variation in the ancient sea floor as the rocks formed. At Abbotsbury, the base of the Kimmeridge Clay is marked by an oolitic ironstone that was once quarried for iron (exposures can be seen in the Red Lane Quarry, a RIGS site just north of the village centre at Grid Ref: SY576853 and along a footpath at Grid Ref: SY576856). In contrast, on the shores of the Fleet near Ferrybridge the equivalent Kimmeridge strata consist of clays that contain a remarkably diverse fossil fauna represented by numerous bone fragments and teeth from fish, crocodiles, ichthyosaurs, flying reptiles and dinosaurs.

The beach below White Nothe is littered with fallen rock; typical of an area exposed to massive landslipping. Fossils, most notably from the chalk, can be found here but they are often difficult to spot. The heart-shaped sea urchin *Micraster* is perhaps the classic chalk fossil, but the bivalve shell *Inoceramus* is far more common and easier to find. Don't be fooled by all the flint that litters the beach. Flint can often appear to resemble many fossils but in reality, there is usually only one fossil to blame, the humble sponge. Sponges once flourished in the chalk sea. Their bodies were made from millions of tiny needles or spicules of silica that created a hollow and porous structure. Upon death, most sponges disintegrated and their spicules were scattered across the sea floor and became buried. After burial, ground water percolating through the rocks dissolved the silica and carried it in solution until it came into contact with other layers rich in sponges. The silica then formed around complete sponges, creating the oddly-shaped and often hollow flints.

THE PURBECK COAST

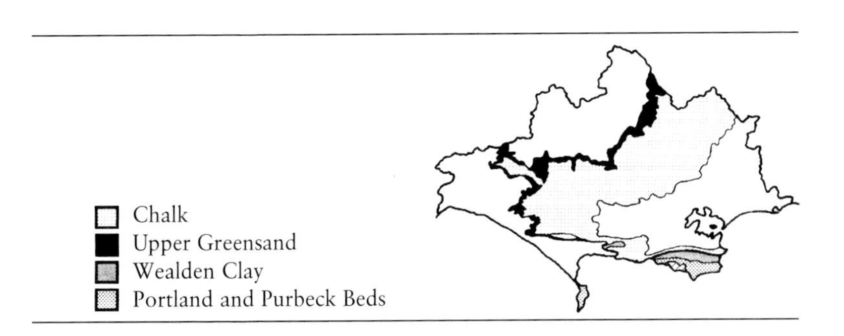

The Purbeck coast stretches from White Nothe, near Ringstead, to the shores of Poole Harbour. As with the rest of Dorset the overall dip of the rocks is eastwards but cutting right across the area is a massive fold, the Purbeck Monocline, which dominates the coast and countryside of Purbeck. The coast displays some of the finest sections of Cretaceous-aged rocks in Britain, while rocks of Jurassic age that are poorly exposed in the west, most notably the Kimmeridge Clay, are magnificently developed here.

Lulworth Cove and Durdle Door have little to tempt the fossil collector but the rocks do contain some extraordinary features, including the well-known Fossil Forest. This area contains the most westerly exposures through the Lower Cretaceous rocks in Dorset. The effect of the Purbeck Monocline is far-reaching, for the rocks have been heaved into a nearly vertical position and have been spectacularly folded – as can be seen in the remarkable Lulworth Crumple in Stair Hole. The Lower Cretaceous rocks in this area are much thinner than the same beds just a little further east. The effect is extreme, in that beds of rock several hundred metres thick in Durlston Bay, Swanage, just fourteen miles to the east, are reduced in thickness to a few tens of metres at Durdle Door.

The complex strata of the Purbeck Beds are spectacularly folded within the headland of Worbarrow Tout. The oddly named Cinder Bed, a layer packed with oyster shells, lies in the foreground.

The Fossil Forest and ripple-bedded limestones can be seen on the landward face of Durdle Door but both are best developed in the cliffs to the east of Lulworth Cove. Just as on the Isle of Portland, the forest consists of doughnut-shaped structures with a hole in the centre where the tree once stood, and formed in the same environments as on Portland. Further east, the forest and associated soils disappear and are replaced by thin layers of shale and clay, indicating that a completely different environment existed here. Unfortunately, the Fossil Forest lies inside the Army Range and is inaccessible when the red flags are flying: the Range is usually open during the school holidays and most weekends.

Still within the Range, Mupe Rocks, Bacon Hole and Worbarrow Bay contain fine exposures through the Purbeck Beds and Wealden Clay, whilst numerous boulders of eroded material lie on the beaches. The Wealden Clay formed in river plains, swamps and lagoons where life was prolific. Some layers contain crumbly black masses of lignite, fossilised wood.

Worbarrow Bay offers one of the finest sections through the

Cretaceous sequence, starting with the chalk of Flowers Barrow and running east to Worbarrow Tout, where layer after layer of Purbeck Beds form a striking coastal feature. The oddly named Cinder Bed is a distinctive horizon packed with oyster shells. The bed indicates a brief return to marine conditions and was once taken to mark the boundary between the Jurassic and Cretaceous rocks. Towards the base of the sequence and the tip of the Tout itself, the Lower Purbeck or Lulworth Beds are dominated by clay rocks and contain lumps of weathered gypsum and ripple-bedded limestones complete with dinosaur footprints.

Great care must be taken within the Ranges as the cliffs are high and unstable. Live ordnance in the form of tank shells and bullets may be encountered on the beaches. Don't touch!

East of Worbarrow, towering strata of Portland Limestone rise steeply from sea level to form Gad Cliff, one of the most spectacular cliffs on the Dorset coast. Between Gad Cliff and Chapman's Pool a virtually complete section through the Kimmeridge Clay is contained within the dark cliffs. This is one of the finest locations in the world to study rocks and fossils of late Jurassic, 'Kimmeridgian' age, an internationally recognised time period whose name has been taken from this stretch of the Dorset coast.

The Kimmeridge Clay marks a return to prolonged, relatively deep water sedimentation, similar to that of the Lower Lias at Lyme Regis. As a result, the area is also famous for large marine reptiles, other vertebrate fossils and even soft-bodied preservation. Well-preserved fossils are much scarcer than in West Dorset, while the commoner fossils such as ammonites are nearly always crushed flat in the soft and crumbly shale.

The one fossil that perhaps excites the imagination more than any other is the huge pliosaur, spectacular remains of which have, and continue to be found. A lower jaw was collected in the 1980's that measures more than five feet in length while teeth up to four inches long have also been found. In contrast, delicate limb bones from flying reptiles, pterosaurs, have also been discovered in recent years and it may only be a matter of time before a complete specimen is uncovered. Ichthyosaurs and fish are also found while recent discoveries include ammonites with what appear to be eggs contained

Complete or even partial pliosaur skeletons are very rare but from their teeth it is clear that they were fearsome predators. These are 8cm long.

within the shell. Carnivorous megalosaur dinosaurs have been discovered, but like so many animals washed from the land, finds normally consist of partial skeletons simply because their corpses were exposed to predation or decay before they sank.

From Chapman's Pool around St Aldhem's Head and on to Durlston, the towering cliffs and buttresses rising vertically out of the sea are formed from the Portland Limestone. Just inland from the coast the Limestone is quarried for two entirely different reasons. St Aldhelm's Quarry was opened to work 'spangle', a beautiful shelly limestone in which the casts of the shells have been filled with calcite crystal and which, once polished, makes a superb decorative stone. In contrast the neighbouring Swanworth Quarry works the Portland Limestone for aggregate.

Moving further east, Durlston Bay contains the finest sequence through the rocks of late Jurassic and early Cretaceous age in Britain and both the Bay and the numerous quarries in the Swanage area are an important source of fossils. The Purbeck Beds are famous for their fauna of fish, amphibians, reptiles, insects and early mammals, the most spectacular being the large dinosaur trackways and individual footprints found on the beach and in the quarries. Complete and

Dinosaur footprints from Keat's Quarry, near Swanage made by large, four legged sauropod dinosaurs. Footprints may be preserved as impressions in the sediment, as in this case, or as a positive cast that fills the depressions made by the footprint.

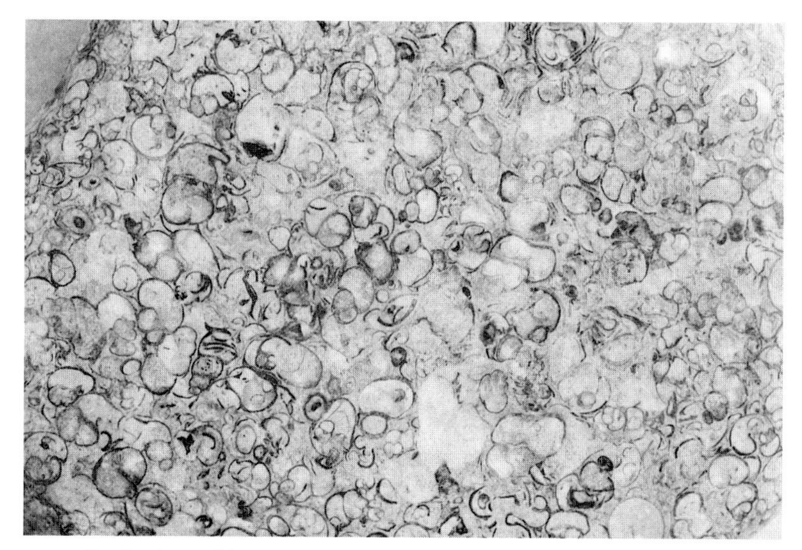

Purbeck Marble is not a true marble but a limestone that takes a fine polish. The rock is composed of a mass of shells including the freshwater gastropod *Viviparus*.

isolated bones of fish, including shark spines, bones from crocodiles and shell fragments of turtles are not uncommon and most quarry offices contain a good collection. The insects are found within a limited number of thin laminated clay strata exposed in the Bay and high up in Swanworth Quarry (the operators, Tarmac do give permission to collect). The rarest finds are those of our early ancestors, the mammals, but their occurrence is sporadic and the technique for finding them involves sieving the sediment and searching for the minute teeth and bone fragments under a microscope.

The commonest fossils, in contrast, are everywhere. Indeed some rocks such as the famous Purbeck Marble are virtually composed of fossils, in this case the shells of freshwater snails. This highly sought after rock is not a true marble but a limestone that takes a fine polish. Originally it was quarried from Peveril Point at the northern end of Durlston Bay, but it has also been worked in the numerous quarrs or mines that riddle the windswept open landscape west of Swanage.

The rocks and fossils of the Purbeck Beds are a great puzzle to geologists in that they provide evidence of many different environments sandwiched closely together bed by bed and displaying great variation across their outcrop. The environment in which they formed was probably similar to the salt flats of Saudi Arabia and other Gulf States, but such a landscape would be too harsh to support the great diversity of life now fossilised within the rocks. It is likely that a more hospitable landmass lay nearby and many of the animals were either washed into the open plains or wandered across them whilst migrating or searching for food. At times the area was flooded, perhaps by subsidence, allowing the sea to rush in. Evaporation then created saline lagoons that eventually dried out.

The Purbeck Marble at Peveril Point is the youngest of the Purbeck Beds. Because it is resistant to erosion, it has created a headland and underwater ledge that extends out to sea, over which the tides race in a spectacular fashion. By contrast, the overlying Wealden Beds together with the Lower and Upper Greensand are soft and have been removed by erosion to create Swanage Bay. The northern side of the Bay is completed by the huge mass of the Chalk which, at Ballard Down, is caught in the Purbeck Monocline that then runs across Poole and Christchurch Bays to join up with the Needles on the Isle of Wight.

Fossils can be found on the beaches just north of Swanage sea front and in Punfield Cove, but their frequency is governed by the natural rate of erosion. The rich fauna of fossil bivalves and snails from the Punfield Marine Band within the Lower Greensand is of particular interest, as is the basal Chalk that contains an extraordinary fauna of uncoiled ammonites such as the bizarre, spiral-shelled *Turrilites*.

STUDLAND TO THE HAMPSHIRE BORDER

Tertiary Clay

Dorset's geology fails to record one of the most momentous events in evolutionary history, the mass extinction of the dinosaurs and some two-thirds of all life on the planet that took place about 65 million years ago at the end of the Cretaceous Period. The reason for this geological missing link is yet another gap in Dorset's rock record, this time between the Cretaceous and Tertiary Periods.

The southern corner of Studland Bay contains the evidence for the gap between the Cretaceous Chalk and the oldest Tertiary Beds, as the junction between the two is marked by an erosion surface. Here the Chalk is deeply weathered and has been dissolved away to create solution holes that have then been filled with younger Tertiary aged pebbles and clays. The gap in the geological record here covers several million years, including the event that caused the extinction of the dinosaurs and which in turn created the opportunity for the mammals to flourish. For this there are many theories, including massive volcanic eruptions in southern India, or the possibility that a huge meteor stuck the earth, blocking out the sun and plunging the planet into a prolonged winter.

The Cretaceous – Tertiary extinction had a profound effect on life on earth, as is clearly illustrated in the fossil record. The Eocene is one age within the Tertiary and owes its name to the Greek for 'dawn' [eos] and 'recent' [kainos], due to the essentially modern fauna and flora found within it. Gone are the dinosaurs, marine reptiles and ammonites and in their place is a fauna very similar to that which exists on the planet today.

The Tertiary Period began some 65 million years ago but only rocks of Eocene age (about 50 to 55 million years old) are found within the county. As with the older Cretaceous and Jurassic rocks, the Tertiary Beds dip gently to the east, creating a fine sequence within the cliffs between Studland and the Hampshire border. Other exposures exist in the low cliffs around Poole Harbour and within the ball clay pits of the area. The rocks are predominantly clays, sands and gravels, giving rise to the distinctive heathland character of this corner of Dorset.

The rocks were formed in deltas and estuaries that were periodically submerged beneath the sea. The Bournemouth Freshwater Beds contain famous fossil plant horizons that have in the past yielded spectacular specimens such as complete palm fronds.

Bournemouth sea front, now heavily protected by sea defences, provides a section through the complete Tertiary rocks of east Dorset.

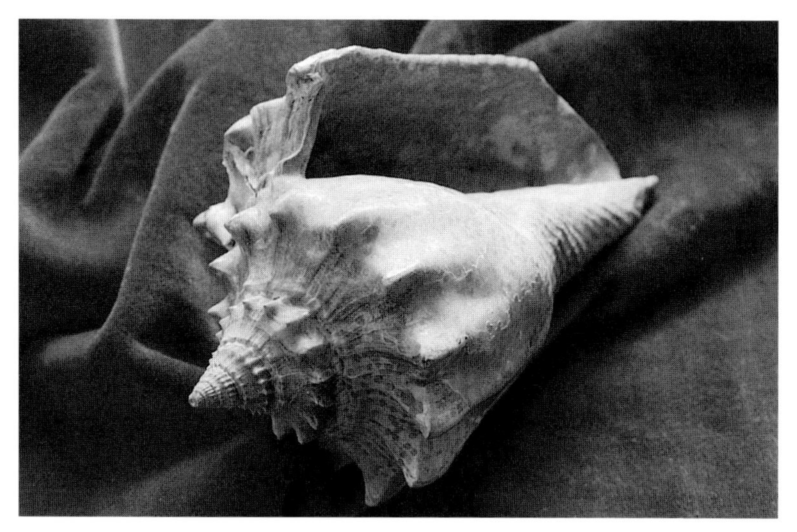

Top The gastropod *Athleta athleta* from the Eocene London Clays at Barton. *Above* Sharks teeth can be abundant on the beaches at Barton, especially after stormy weather.

Collecting along Bournemouth sea front today is clearly no longer an option, but the County Museum in Dorchester and the Bournemouth Natural Sciences Society hold good collections and have specimens on display.

The richest Tertiary strata are the marine London Clays and Barton, on the Dorset-Hampshire border, provides the best collecting locality. The fauna here is extensive and includes numerous gastropods and bivalves, fish remains and sharks teeth.

THE LAST CHAPTER?

In the last two million years Dorset has been subjected to the last Ice Age and great fluctuations in the climate. The river gravels of the Stour have revealed elephants while other large mammal bones have been recovered from fissure infills on Portland. At low tide, a fossil forest is occasionally exposed at Charmouth and consists of tree trunks, twigs, hazelnuts and occasional mammal bones such as deer. It provides evidence for lower sea levels, perhaps linked to colder weather and a larger ice cap. At Portland Bill, a raised beach contains gastropod shells and records a time when sea levels were higher.

These may be the youngest fossils within the county but their story is far from over. Even as you read this, somewhere on the sea bed an animal such as a dead shark or dolphin is being buried by silt or mud alongside traces of ourselves. For it is not inconceivable that a whole range of man-made objects, even the sunken remains of shipwrecks, will become buried, creating trace fossils of mankind. Millions of years from now these objects will appear 'instantaneously' in the fossil record, providing clues to what will then be the ancient 'past'. More worryingly, they will also record the rapid extinction now taking place as a result of our impact on the planet.

Perhaps such pessimism is misplaced ? The fossil record makes it clear that life on earth has faced many challenges, and has so far robustly shrugged them aside. The present threats posed by global warming and the rise in the sea level are more a concern for us than the planet. Life will survive and flourish despite our worst excesses, though the replacement of one species by another will take millions of years. The great Cretaceous/Tertiary extinction wiped out the dinosaurs but created the right conditions for the mammals to evolve, including ourselves. If there is one lesson the fossil record teaches us, it is the need to safeguard the rich bio-diversity that surrounds us today, not for the planet's benefit but our own.

FURTHER READING

The British Natural History Museum's handbooks *British Mesozoic Fossils* and *British Caenozoic Fossils* offer the best introduction to the full range of specimens to be found within the county.

The Charmouth Heritage Coast Centre publish an information leaflet called *Charmouth and Lyme Regis Fossil Guide.*

Arkell, J. W., *The Geology of the Country around Weymouth, Swanage, Corfe and Lulworth* (Memoir of the Geological Survey, HMSO), 1947

Bristow, C. R., Barton, C. M., Freshney, E. C., Wood, C. J., Evans, D. J., Cox, B. M., Ivimey-Cook, H. C. and Taylor, R. T., *Geology of the Country around Shaftesbury* (Memoir of the Geological Survey, HMSO),1995

Bristow, C. R., Freshney, E. C. and Penn, I. E., *Geology of the Country around Bournemouth* (Memoir of the Geological Survey, HMSO), 1991

Ensom, P., *Discover Dorset: Geology* (Dovecote Press), 1998

House, M. R., *The Geology of the Dorset Coast* (Geologist Association Guide, 2nd Edition), 1993

Melville, R. V. And Freshney, E. C., *British Regional Geology: The Hampshire Basin and adjoining Areas* (6th Edition) (HMSO)

Norman, D. *The Illustrated Encyclopaedia of Dinosaurs* (Guild Publishing), 1985

Rowe S. R. and Torrens H. S., *Ichthyosaurs: a history of 'sea dragons'* (National Museum of Wales)

Wilson, V., Welsh, F. B. A., Robbie, J. A. and Green, G. W., *Geology of the Country around Bridport and Yeovil* (Memoir of the Geological Survey, HMSO), 1958

A comprehensive *Bibliography and index of Dorset Geology* by Jo Thomas and Paul Ensom, 1988, is available from the Dorset County Museum, Dorchester.

The Proceedings of the Dorset Natural History and Archaeological Society are published annually and frequently contain articles and notes on Dorset's fossils and geology. The society is based at the County Museum, Dorchester and offprints are generally available at the museum shop.

The Bournemouth Natural Sciences Society holds a collection and library on Dorset's geology and fossils, on both of which they hold frequent lectures.

Southampton University provides extensive information on Dorset's geology through their web site at; **www.soton.ac.uk/~imw/index.htm.**

Geological maps of the county are published by the British Geological Survey and can be acquired by contacting the Sales Desk, BGS, Kingsley Dunham Centre, Keyworth, Nottingham NG12 5GG.

Dorset Important Geological/Geomorphological Sites Group identify and manage Regionally Important Geological/Gcomorphological Sites (RIGS) in Dorset. Information about such sites can be obtained by writing to them at the Dorset Wildlife Trust, Brooklands Farm, Forston, Dorchester DT2 7AA.

Rockwatch, also through the Dorset Wildlife Trust, provides an exciting programme of events for children and their parents.

Dorset Geologist's Association organises a programme of walks and events including the annual Wimborne Fossil and Mineral Fair in August.

The Dorset Countryside Book, published annually by Dorset County Council, Countryside Service, contains over 350 guided walks across the county including all aspects of county's geology. Available at Tourist Information and visitor Centres throughout the county.

ACKNOWLEDGEMENTS

I would like to thank the following fossil collectors for their willingness to allow me to photograph so many of their fossils for use in talks, interactive displays and now this book: Bernie & Rose Abbott: page 6 (top); Adrian Brokenshire: page 4, 28, 33 (bottom), 57 (top), 63, 65, 70, 76 (both); Charmouth Heritage Coast Centre: page 31; Andy Cowap: page 21, 23 (top); Tony Gill: page 48 (bottom); Steve Etches: page 6 (bottom); Chris Moore: page 23 (bottom), 27 (bottom), 52 (the latter with thanks also to David Costin and J. Toms) 53; Old Forge Fossil Co.: page 30, 47.

I am also grateful to the following for allowing the inclusion of illustrations for which they hold the copyright: Natural History Museum, London: page 25; The Dovecote Press Collection: page 14; Paul Ensom: page 71; The Geological Society of London: page 43; Jo Thomas: page 72.

I would like to thank Paul Ensom and Bryan Meloy for their comments on the geological content, David Burnett for the chance to write this book, and Christopher Chaplin for drawing the maps.

Finally, I wish to thank my mother, Jackie, for her constant support and encouragement.

The

DISCOVER DORSET

Series of Books

A series of paperback books providing informative illustrated introductions to Dorset's history, culture and way of life. The following titles have so far been published.

BRIDGES *David McFetrich and Jo Parsons*
CASTLES AND FORTS *Colin Pomeroy* COAST & SEA *Sarah Welton*
CRANBORNE CHASE *Desmond Hawkins*
DOWNS, MEADOWS & PASTURES *Jim White*
DRESS AND TEXTILES *Rachel Worth*
FARMHOUSES AND COTTAGES *Michael Billett*
FARMING *J.H.Bettey* FOLLIES *Jonathan Holt*
FOSSILS *Richard Edmonds* GEOLOGY *Paul Ensom*
THE GEORGIANS *Jo Draper* HEATHLANDS *Lesley Haskins*
THE INDUSTRIAL PAST *Peter Stanier*
ISLE OF PURBECK *Paul Hyland*
LEGENDS *Jeremy Harte* LOST VILLAGES *Linda Viner*
MILLS *Peter Stanier*
PORTLAND *Stuart Morris* POTTERY *Penny Copland-Griffiths*
THE PREHISTORIC AGE *Bill Putnam*
RAILWAY STATIONS *Mike Oakley*
REGENCY, RIOT AND REFORM *Jo Draper*
RIVERS & STREAMS *John Wright* THE ROMANS *Bill Putnam*
SAXONS AND VIKINGS *David Hinton*
SHIPWRECKS *Maureen Attwooll* STONE QUARRYING *Jo Thomas*
THE VICTORIANS *Jude James* WOODLANDS *Anne Horsfall*

All the books about Dorset published by The Dovecote Press are available in bookshops throughout the county, or in case of difficulty direct from the publishers.